TOM PAXTON
RAMBLIN' BOY
and other songs

ORIGINAL DRAWINGS BY AGNES FRIESEN

Oak Publications
New York • London • Tokyo • Sydney • Cologne

Illustrations by Agnes Friesen

Cover design by Ronald Clyne

Music edited by Milt Okun

Production editor: Ethel Raim

Production assistant: Jean Hammons

International Standard Book Number: 0-8256-0007-3
Library of Congress Catalog Card Number: 65-26580

Distributed throughout the world by Music Sales Corporation:

33 West 60th Street, New York 10023
78 Newman Street, London W1P 3LA
4-26-22 Jingumae, Shibuya-ku, Tokyo 150
27 Clarendon Street, Artarmon, Sydney NSW 2064
Kölner Strasse 199, D-5000, Cologne 90

CONTENTS

INTRODUCTION

I. TOPICAL & PROTEST SONGS

9 The Thresher Disaster
10 The Great American Dream
12 Six Men Riding
13 When Morning Breaks
14 I Read It in "The Daily
                    News"
16 There Was A Time
17 A Job of Work to Do
18 The Willing Conscript
20 The Dogs of Alabama
21 Strange Rain
22 The High Sheriff of Hazard
24 What Did You Learn in
                    School Today?
27 Standing on the Edge of
                    Town
28 A Rumbling in the Land

II. CHILDREN'S SONGS

33 Little Brand New Baby
34 Going to the Zoo
36 Let's Pretend
38 My Dog's Bigger Than
                    Your Dog
40 The Marvelous Toy

III. STORY SONGS

45 Willie Seton
46 John, John, John
48 I'm the Man That Built
                    the Bridges

IV. YOU'VE GOT TO FEEL BAD
SOMETIMES

53 Deep Fork River Blues
54 I Can't Help But Wonder
                    (Where I'm Bound)
56 Come Along Home
57 Ramblin' Boy
59 Rain and Snow
60 I'm on My Last Old Train
61 I'm Bound for the Mountain
                    and the Sea
62 Fare Thee Well, Cisco

V. FURTHER PILLS TO PURGE
MELANCHOLY

67 Bottle of Wine
68 I Happen to Like Whiskey,
                    Sir!
70 The Natural Girl for Me
72 I'm Going to the Limelight
                    to Die
74 The N. Y. Mets Victory and
                    Commiseration Song
75 Willie My Weaver-O
76 The Meanest Man in the
                    World

VI. LOVE SONGS

81 My Lady's A Wild Flying
                    Dove
83 Ev'ry Time (When We Are
                    Gone)
84 Please Let Me Stay With
                    You
85 The Last Thing on My
                    Mind

INTRODUCTION

I have a habit - the habit of sitting in Joe's on West Fourth Street or the kitchen of the Gaslight or in my genuine Danish three-geared reclining chair, trying to carry on the work that Woody began. The reference to Guthrie is no accident, for those of us who write songs today (Dylan, Chandler, Marrs, Ochs, LaFarge, Reynolds, Spoelstra, et al) owe it all to Woody. He showed us how and he told us why.

I've been writing songs for six years; my beginning efforts were turned out during Shakespeare lectures at the University of Oklahoma. No eyes but mine shall ever look upon those poor pitiful babes. I wrote my first "keeper" in 1960 while taking the clerk-typist course at Ft. Dix, N.J. The song was "The Marvelous Toy" and I was unsure of it. The first person to like it and tell me so was the poet Ed Freeman, whose work I admired so much and who died tragically in a plane crash in South America a few years ago. He loved the ancient South American cultures and his plane crashed into some old ruin. But that, indeed, is another story.

In the Fall of 1960 I met Milt Okun. I was trying for a spot in The Chad Mitchell Trio, which I didn't get, but I did sing "Toy" for Milt, their musical director, and he asked if he could arrange it for them. He also asked me to write more, which was foolhardy, for I began calling him at very weird hours to sing him new songs over the phone. Looking back, his patience with me was astonishing and he gave me the encouragement I so badly needed.

I am resisting the impulse to write one of those endless dedication things that nobody reads anyhow, but my resistance is weakening, so I'd better cut it short. My mother deserves my thanks for never insisting on my becoming a doctor. I would have been a kindly, attentive and sincere doctor - and devastatingly incompetent.

Tradition is the life-blood of folk music, and it's traditional to dedicate a book like this to one's wife, should one happen to have a wife, which I do. She's a really special one, is Midge, and of more help to me than I could ever say.

As for the songs, they're the best of what I've done so far. I hope you like them but, more importantly, I hope you enjoy singing them. If you like them on the printed page but don't sing them - then I will have failed.

I'm proud of the whole legion of songwriters springing up. Every time Len or Bob or whoever turns out a new one, it spurs me on to try to do the same to them. Here's to the songwriters yet to come.

Are they folk songs? Depends on your definition, really. Personally, I think it takes years to know for sure. Maybe a couple of these songs will hang around for a little while at least. I hope so.

Tom Paxton
New York City
Winter 1964-65

I.

TOPICAL and PROTEST SONGS

The Thresher Disaster - melody based on Jesse James. Everybody knows the story.

The Great American Dream - You've heard of it, of course. All about life, liberty, the pursuit of happiness - all that idealistic stuff.

Six Men Riding - Which war? Any war. We could have used the men who never made it back.

When Morning Breaks - Always they go,
            the proud young men,
     The singing men, the best young men,
     And when will they ever come back again.
     And when will we have to send more?

I Read It In The Daily News - Just a couple of weeks ago they ran an editorial wondering why in hell we hadn't dropped an A-bomb on Moscow in 1945, when we had the opportunity. And failing that, what was holding us back with Cuba? This is the paper with the largest circulation in the U.S.

There Was A Time - It began with rocks and clubs. With the invention of the spear they all agreed that war was now impossible, for here was a weapon too terrible ever to be used.

A Job Of Work To Do - These people down in Hazard, Ky., don't want handouts. They want to go to work, but the only jobs offered are in the unsafe "dog holes" for scab wages: $3.00 to $8.00 a day.

The Willing Conscript - I wrote this at Dave Wilson's house in Cambridge, Mass., after swapping tales of the war-lovers and glorifiers.

The Dogs of Alabama - You probably saw the pictures last year, unless you only read Southern newspapers. They still have the dogs but they got rid of Bull.

Strange Rain - I did this one in Toronto in 1962 and recorded it with Gil Robbins. Since then we've had the test ban, but they've still got them stacked up somewhere, waiting.

The High Sheriff of Hazard - Ewan MacColl used this tune The Limerick Rake, for Champion At Keeping Them Rolling. Perry County, Kentucky, is run by and for a few people. Anyone urging changes is an agitator and a communist. The hunting season on communists never closes. Communists can be identified either by their out of state license tags or by association with the native-born agitators.

What Did You Learn In School? - Like many kids, I resented learning that I'd been put on by the Washington-never-lied-cherry-tree nonsense. The truth is much more fascinating and a damned sight more worth the having. Milt Okun did a beautiful arrangement of this one for The Chad Mitchell Trio, and Pete Seeger did it in his great We Shall Overcome album.

Standing On the Edge of Town - Automation could be the greatest thing ever to come down the pike, but as it is a lot of people are losing jobs - and the automating process has barely begun. I tried to look through the eyes of one man who's tried to figure it all out by himself.

A Rumbling In The Land - And those who can't hear it won't understand Bob Dylan's The Times They Are A-Changing either.

The Thresher Disaster

Words and Music by Tom Paxton © 1963 by Cherry Lane Music Inc.

Oh we had a sub-mar-ine, She was might-y fast and lean, And she ran by a-tom-ic pow-er, too. And al-though she was the best, They had one more div-ing test So the "Thresh-er" could show what she could do.

Chorus

And she's gone, gone, gone, to the bot-tom of the sea, And she's two hun-dred miles from the shore. It was just a div-ing test, But they laid her there to rest on the cold and lone-some o-cean floor.

Now those boys were still alive
When she started in to dive
For she radioed that she was goin'
    down
What went wrong we cannot say
But it was later on that day
That the flotsam and the oil slick
    were found. (Chorus)

Although none of them was mine
We lost a hundred twenty-nine
And I feel just like I lost a friend
And I sit and wonder why
Those poor sailors had to die
And I wonder when this killin's
    gonna end. (Chorus)

The Great American Dream

Words and Music by Tom Paxton © 1963 by Cherry Lane Music Inc.

Have you seen the long grass wav-ing in the past-ures in the spring? Have you seen the gold-en mead-ow-larks and heard the songs they sing? Have you dived in-to the wa-ters of an i-cy moun-tain stream? Have you shared with your fore-fa-thers in The great A-mer-i-can dream? In the

Chorus

great A-mer-i-can dream, the great A-mer-i-can dream, Have you shared with your fore-fa-thers in the great A-mer-i-can dream?

Did you see the peaches bloomin' by
  the churchyard at Shiloh?
Did you fight the river pirates on the
  rolling Ohio?
Have you ever lost your pasture in a
  roaring prairie fire?
Have you ever won a strike and found
  the prices getting higher?

Chorus:
Found the prices getting higher, the
  prices getting higher,
Have you ever won a strike and found
  the prices getting higher?

Were you in the bloody battles of the
  bloody Pullman strike?
Were you at Corregidor and did you
  make that bloody hike?
Were you down in Mississippi? Did
  you face that jeering mob?
Were you mining down at Hazard when
  they took away your job?

Chorus:
When they took away your job, they
  took away your job,
Were you mining down in Hazard when
  they took away your job?

10

Have you stood and watched the dust
    storms on the Oklahoma plains?
Have you rode with the jobless
    migrants on the rattlin' flat-car
    trains?
Have you ever been blacklisted by a
    silent poison pen?
Have you ever heard the talkin' of a
    gang of hungry men?

Chorus:
Of a gang of hungry men, a gang of
    hungry men,
Have you ever heard the talkin' of a
    gang of hungry men?

Did you ever dream of spending time
    with your own family?
And watch your kids a-growin' up and
    feelin' that you're free?
Do you very often wonder if things are
    what they seem?
Do you wonder what is happening to
    your great American dream?

Chorus:
To your great American dream, your
    great American dream,
Do you wonder what is happening to
    your great American dream?

Six Men Riding

Words and Music by Tom Paxton ©1962 by Cherry Lane Music Inc.

Six men lately from the war,
Six men fought so bravely,
Six men coming home again,
Six remain from eighty
Six men out of eighty lived
Six men out of eighty. (Refrain)

Six men home to sow the fields
Six to plant the corn
Six pretty ladies to weep for joy
And seventy-four to mourn
Seventy-four to mourn and weep
Seventy-four to mourn. (Refrain)

When Morning Breaks

Words and Music by Tom Paxton © 1962 by Cherry Lane Music Inc.

13

I Read It in "The Daily News"

Words and Music by Tom Paxton © 1964 by Deep Fork Music Inc.

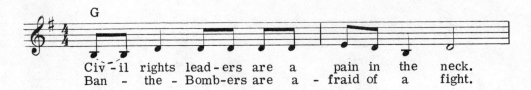

Civ - il rights lead - ers are a pain in the neck.
Ban - the - Bomb - ers are a - fraid of a fight.

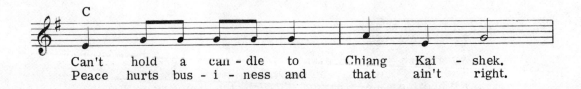

Can't hold a can - dle to Chiang Kai - shek.
Peace hurts bus - i - ness and that ain't right.

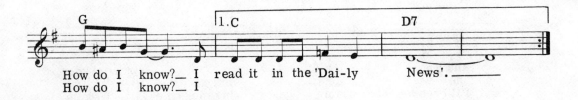

How do I know?_ I read it in the 'Dai - ly News'._
How do I know?_ I

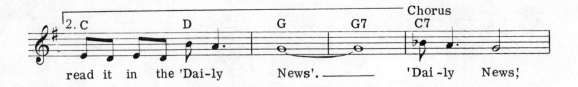

read it in the 'Dai - ly News'._ 'Dai - ly News,'

Dai - ly blues, Pick up a co - py an - y time you choose.

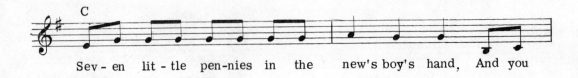

Sev - en lit - tle pen - nies in the new's boy's hand, And you

ride right a - long to nev - er nev - er land.

14

We got to bomb Castro, got to bomb
    him flat,
He's too damned successful and we
    can't risk that,
How do I know? I read it in the Daily
    News.
There's millions of commies in the
    Freedom Fight,
Yellin' for Lenin and Civil Rights,
How do I know? I read it in the Daily
    News. (Chorus)

Seems like the whole damned world's
    gone wrong,
St. Joe McCarthy is dead and gone,
How do I know? I read it in the Daily
    News.
Don't try to change my mind with facts,
To Hell with the graduated income tax!
How do I know? I read it in the Daily
    News. (Chorus)

John Paul Getty is just plain folks
The UN Charter is a cruel hoax
How do I know? I read it in the Daily
    News.
J. Edgar Hoover is the man of the
    hour,
All that he needs is just a little more
    power,
How do I know? I read it in the Daily
    News. (Chorus)

There Was A Time

Words and Music by Tom Paxton © 1962 by Cherry Lane Music Inc.

1. There was a time ____ when can - nons roared ____ ____ And bu - gles sang ____ a song of war ____ And na - tions rose ____ ____ to win or die ____ They shook the earth ____ with bat - tle cries.
2. The ci - ties fell ____ in smoke and flames ____ ____ And chil - dren cried ____ their moth-ers' names ____ And na - tions died ____ ____ and were no more ____ The vic - tors were ____ the gods of war.
3. They left their homes ____ and went to war ____ ____ And died up - on ____ some for - eign shore ____ Their sons grew tall ____ ____ and soon were men ____ And bu - gles sang ____ their songs a - gain.

Chorus
And I can hear ____ their spi - rits cry ____ This was a cru - el way to die! The spi - rits of ____ ____ these fal - len men ____ Re - minds us of ____ what might have been.

A Job of Work to Do

Words and Music by Tom Paxton © 1964 by Deep Fork Music Inc.

I hate un-em-ploy-ment and I'll tell you why, I want to keep work-ing til the day I die, I like to work, I do it well and when I can't feed my fam-'ly, Lord, I feel like hell.

Chorus

Lord, give me a job of work to do.

Lord, give me a job of work to do That's all I want, that's all I ask of You.

The government man, he says its fine
To go on down to the free food line.
Nice of the government to be so fair
But I don't want my friends to see me
    there. (Chorus)

I was born and raised in these old
    hills,
I never left 'em and I never will.
I'm able-bodied and my friends are,
    too,
And all we ask is a job to do.
    (Chorus)

Yes, these are the worst times I have
    seen,
Don't want to seem ungrateful or
    mean,
But a man's got to raise his family
And I can't stand to raise 'em on
    charity. (Chorus)

The Willing Conscript

Words and Music by Tom Paxton © 1963 by Cherry Lane Music Inc.

Oh, serg-eant I'm a draft-ee and I've just ar-rived in camp.__I've come to wear the un-i-form and join the mar-tial tramp._____ And I want to do my du-ty but one thing I do im-plore__You must give me les-sons, serg-eant, for I've nev-er killed be-fore. __

To do my job obediently is my only
  desire.
To learn my weapon thoroughly and
  how to aim and fire.
To learn to kill the enemy and then
  to slaughter more,
I'll need instruction, Sergeant, for
  I've never killed before.

Now there are several lessons that
  I haven't mastered yet.
I haven't got the hang of how to use the
  bayonet.
If he doesn't die at once am I to stick
  him with it more?
Oh, I hope you will be patient, for I've
  never killed before.

Oh, there are rumors in the camp
  about our enemy.
They say that when you see him he
  looks just like you and me.
But you deny it, Sergeant, and you
  are a man of war,
So you must give me lessons, for
  I've never killed before.

The hand grenade is something that I
  just don't understand.
You've got to throw it quickly or you're
  apt to lose your hand.
Does it blow a man to pieces with its
  wicked, muffled roar?
Oh, I've got so much to learn because
  I've never killed before.

18

Oh, I want to thank you, Sergeant, for
        the help you've been to me.
For you've taught me how to slaughter
        and to hate the enemy.
And I know that I'll be ready when they
        march me off to war,
And I know that it won't matter that
        I've never killed before,
And I know that it won't matter that
        I've never killed before.

AF

The Dogs of Alabama

Words and Music by Tom Paxton © 1963 by Cherry Lane Music Inc.

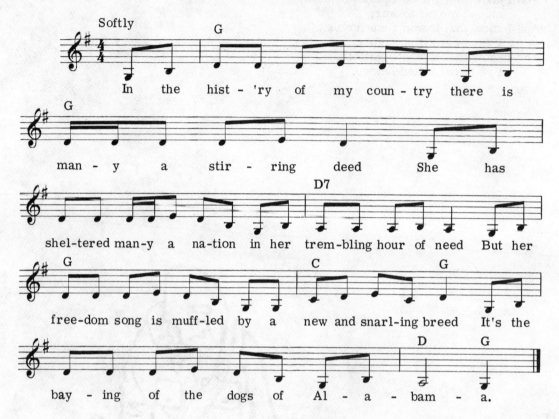

In a happy pack they travel for they
  dare not stand alone,
And their tails are gaily wagging, as
  they dream of flesh and bone,
And they plan their preservation in
  the comfort of their homes,
Do the baying of the dogs of
  Alabama.

The people down in Birmingham, they
  don't care much for strikes,
And the roaring bull who leads them
  hates all nigger-lovin' kikes,
And he don't know much about freedom
  but he knows just what he likes,
He likes his faithful dogs of
  Alabama.

Oh, they love old Uncle Tom, they
  love to see him dance and run,
And they love to see him sweating as
  he labors in the sun,
And if they hang one now and then it's
  just good honest fun,
For those rip-roaring dogs of
  Alabama.

When the status quo is troubled and
  the peace you must defend,
You can use high-pressure hoses and
  your troopers without end,
But if you'd really do the trick, just
  call in man's best friend,
Call your merry, merry, dogs of
  Alabama.

Strange Rain

Words and Music by Tom Paxton, © 1962 by Calliope, Inc.,   assigned
1962 by Cherry Lane Music, Inc.

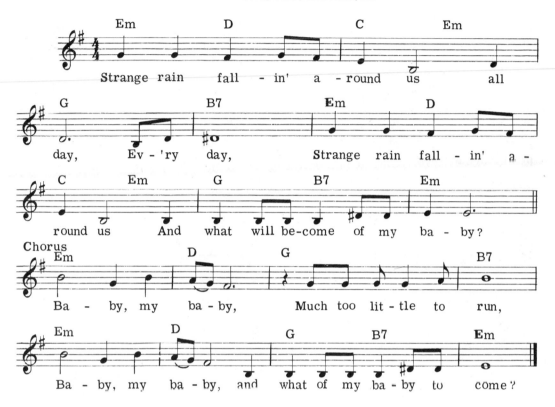

Strange rain fall - in' a - round us all day, Ev - 'ry day, Strange rain fall - in' a - round us And what will be-come of my ba - by?

Chorus

Ba - by, my ba - by, Much too lit - tle to run, Ba - by, my ba - by, and what of my ba - by to come?

They are measurin' death for a suit,
    Lord,
All day, Every day,
They're measurin' death for a suit,
    Lord,
And what will become of my baby?

We had the wrong kind of umbrella
All day, every day,
We had the wrong kind of umbrella,
And what will become of my baby?

(Now My) Kids don't eat what I feed
    'em,
All day, every day,
My kids don't eat what I feed 'em,
And what will become of my baby?

The High Sheriff of Hazard

Words and Music by Tom Paxton © 1964 by Deep Fork Music Inc.

He caught me one evening and here's
    what he said:
"You look like a Russian, you look
    like a Red,
And If you are fond of your skin and
    your head,
Beware the high sheriff of Hazard."

I thanked him politely, I thanked him
    for all,
And five minutes later I made a phone
    call,
To call a strike meeting at our union
    hall
And damn the high sheriff of Hazard.

Now, men there are plenty who sweat
    out their lives,
To scratch out a living for children
    and wives.
They sweat for their pennies while the
    mine owner thrives
With the blessings of the high sheriff
    of Hazard.

And when union men strike and the
    troubles come on,
The high sheriff's word is the mine
    owners' bond,
He's a mine owner, too; you know
    which side he's on,
He's the wealthy high sheriff of
    Hazard.

It seems to be so since this world
    first began,
That some men are willing to scheme
    and to plan,
To gouge out a fortune from the poor
    working man,
For example, the high sheriff of
    Hazard.

But the answer is simple, the
    answer is clear,
Let's all get together with nothing to
    fear,
And throw the old bastard right out
    on his ear,
Farewell to the high sheriff of
    Hazard.

What Did You Learn in School Today?

Words and Music by Tom Paxton © 1962 by Teena Music Corp.

What did you learn in school today,
Dear little boy of mine?
What did you learn in school today,
Dear little boy of mine?
I learned that policemen are my
        friends
I learned that justice never ends,
I learned that murderers die for their
        crimes,
Even if we make a mistake sometimes,
And that's what I learned in school
        today,
That's what I learned in school.

What did you learn in school today,
Dear little boy of mine?
What did you learn in school today,
Dear little boy of mine?
I learned that war is not so bad,
I learned of the great ones we had
        had,
We fought in Germany and in France,
And someday I might get my chance,
And that's what I learned in school
        today,
That's what I learned in school.

What did you learn in school today,
Dear little boy of mine?
What did you learn in school today,
Dear little boy of mine?
I learned our government must be
        strong,
It's always right and never wrong,
Our leaders are the finest men,
And we elect them again and again,
And that's what I learned in school
        today,
That's what I learned in school.

AF

Standing on the Edge of Town

Words and Music by Tom Paxton © 1964 by Deep Fork Music Inc.

I was doing just great, never showed
    up late,
I did all a man could do.
Till I found a note in my pay envelope
Saying: "That's all she wrote for
    you." (Chorus)

Well, I guess I'm lucky 'cause I've
    got no kids,
And I'm one of those bachelor men,
But Jimmy's got four and Billy's got
    two,
And I sure feel bad about them.
    (Chorus)

Well, they've got a machine where I
    used to stand,
Just as funny looking as can be.
Saying: "Sorry, boys, but you have
    to go."
That meant Jimmy and Billy and me.
    (Chorus)

That machine is pretty and it's fast
    as the Devil,
But there's just one thing I see,
You can bet the Boss, he didn't take
    no loss;
It was Jimmy and Billy and me.
    (Chorus)

A Rumbling in the Land

Words and Music by Tom Paxton © 1963 by Deep Fork Music Inc.

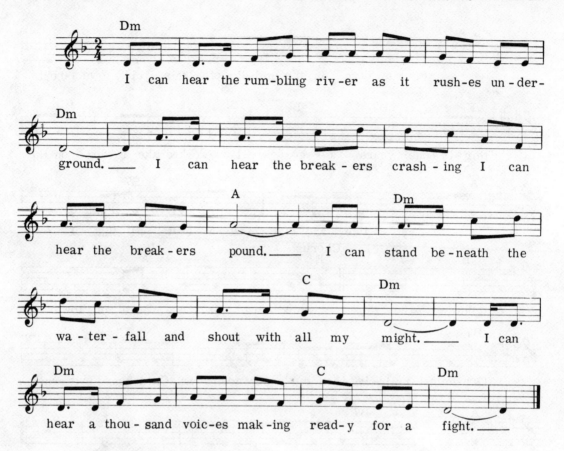

I can hear the rum-bling riv-er as it rush-es un-der-ground. ___ I can hear the break-ers crash-ing I can hear the break-ers pound. ___ I can stand be-neath the wa-ter-fall and shout with all my might. ___ I can hear a thou-sand voic-es mak-ing read-y for a fight. ___

I can ride through Colorado in a
   semi-trailer cab.
I can hang around the truck-stops; I
   can hear them joke and gab.
I can hear them telling stories of the
   lives that they must lead,
As they wonder how they'll make it
   with so many mouths to feed.

I can see the share-crop farmer as
   he wipes his sweaty brow.
He can see the crop's a-failin', but it
   ain't his, anyhow.
I can see the dust a-swirling on his
   played-out farming land,
And I see him hunker down and let it
   trickle through his hand.

I can listen to the hobo as he shuffles
   down the street.
I can hear him in the diner as he bums
   a bite to eat.
For ten years he stoked a furnace till
   the fact'ry whistle blowed,
Got laid off by automation and it put
   him on the road.

And I met another fellow as I
   wandered all about.
He was mining down at Hazard till his
   union sold him out.
Yes, they worked him in the coal
   mine till his back and arms were
   sore,
Then they put him on the blacklist, and
   he can't go back no more.

And I met a fine young Negro lad,
     about seventeen or so.
He didn't like those Southern jails,
     but he felt he had to go,
Saying, "Mom and Dad were Negroes
     and my son will be one, too,
And I guess it's up to me because
     we've given up on you."

And as I passed an Air Force base a
     young man I did meet
With his shiny wings of silver and his
     uniform so neat,
Saying, "I don't want to bomb them,
     Sir, it fills me with dismay,
But orders they are orders and you
     know I must obey."

I've been traveling through this country
     and my eyes are open wide,
And the things I've seen and heard you
     couldn't imagine if you tried.
I've been listening to the people and
     one thing I understand:
A great flood is rising fast and there's
     a rumbling in the land.

AF

II.

CHILDREN'S SONGS

<u>Little Brand New Baby</u> - Greetings to a spanking, squalling, crawling new bundle of humanity - in this case the son of my friend, Milt Okun.

<u>Going To The Zoo</u>- I must confess that I'm still a sucker for the zoo. Half the fun is watching the kids watch the animals.

<u>Let's Pretend</u> - I wish we could figure out what becomes of our imagination as we grow up. Must have something to do with tight collars.

<u>My Dog's Bigger Than Your Dog</u> - Wanna make something of it?

<u>The Marvelous Toy</u> - I can't tell you any more about what it looks like - that's up to you.

Little Brand New Baby

(For Andrew Arthur Okun, born September 29, 1962.)

Words and Music by Tom Paxton © 1962 by Cherry Lane Music Inc.

Hey, lit - tle brand new ba - by, ____ Your mom - ma and your dad - dy ____ think you're might - y nice.

Hey, lit - tle brand new ba - by, ____ I hope you have a might - y nice life. ____

Your dad - dy's ____ look - in' might - y proud, Hand - in' out cig - ars all a - round the town, Grin - nin' like a pos - sum and I think he's gon - na crow, And I hope you have a might - y nice life. ____

It all lies ahead of you and from this
day
It won't be easy as you travel your
way,
But here's to your birth and I just want
to say
That I hope you have a mighty nice
life.

Your momma waited quite awhile,
Carried you around for half a million
miles,
But you know it was worth it when you
look at her smile,
And I hope you have a mighty nice
life.

33

Going to the Zoo

Words and Music by Tom Paxton © 1961 by Cherry Lane Music Inc.

See the elephant with the long trunk
    swingin'
Great big ears and long trunk swingin'
Sniffin' up peanuts with the long trunk
    swingin'
We can stay all day. (Chorus)

Big black bear all huff huff a-puffin'
Coat's too heavy, he's huff huff
    a-puffin'
Don't get too near the huff huff
    a-puffin'
Or you won't stay all day. (Chorus)

See all the monkeys scritch,
    scritch scratchin'
Jumpin' all around and scritch,
    scritch scratchin'
Hangin' by their long tails scritch,
    scritch scratchin'
We can stay all day. (Chorus)

Seals in the pool all honk honk
    honkin'
Catchin' fish and honk honk honkin'
Little seals honk honk honkin'
    (high pitched voice)
We can stay all day. (Chorus)

AF

(Slower Tempo)
We stayed all day and I'm gettin'
    sleepy
Sittin' in the car gettin' sleep sleep
    sleepy
Home already and I'm sleep sleep
    sleepy
We have stayed all day.

Chorus:
We've been to the zoo zoo zoo
So have you you you
You came too too too
We've been to the zoo zoo zoo.

(Up Tempo)
Mamma's taking us to the zoo
    tomorrow
Zoo tomorrow, zoo tomorrow,
Momma's taking us to the zoo
    tomorrow,
We can stay all day.

Chorus:
We're going to the zoo, zoo, zoo
How about you, you, you,
You can come too, too, too,
We're going to the zoo, zoo, zoo.

Let's Pretend

Words and Music by Tom Paxton © 1963 by Cherry Lane Music Inc.

Chorus

Let's pre-tend just you and me,

be what-ev-er you want to be,

You will be my se-cret friend, And we'll play Let's Pre-tend.

Verse

1. Let's be a p'lice-man, p'lice-man, p'lice-man, Let's be a p'lice-man now,

Blow your whis-tle as loud as you can

Catch the burg-a-lar, burg-a-lar man

Take him a-way and throw him in the can Let's be a p'lice-man now.

Let's be a teacher, teacher, teacher
Let's be a teacher now
Teaching all the A B C's
Write on the blackboard big as you
    please
These are the leaves and these are
    the trees
Let's be a teacher now.

Let's be a monkey, monkey, monkey
Let's be a monkey now
Hang 'way up in a monkey tree
Make a funny face and scratch your
    knee
Best little monkey that you ever did
    see
Let's be a monkey now.

Let's be a gray wolf, gray wolf, gray
    wolf
Let's be a gray wolf now
Growlin' wolf on four gray feet
Mean and ugly and not very sweet
Lookin' for somethin' nice to eat
Let's be a gray wolf now.

AF

My Dog's Bigger Than Your Dog

Words and Music by Tom Paxton ©1962 by Cherry Lane Music Inc.

My dog's bigger than your dog,
My dog's bigger than yours,
My dog's bigger
And he chases mailmen,
My dog's bigger than yours.

My dad's tougher than your dad,
My dad's tougher than yours,
My dad's tougher
And he yells louder and
My dad's tougher than yours.

Answering Verses

My dog's better than your dog,
My dog's better than yours,
His name is King,
And he had puppies,
My dog's better than yours.

My dad's louder than your dad,
My dad's louder than yours,
Momma buys a new dress,
Daddy makes noises,
My dad's louder than yours.

Our car's faster than your car,
Our car's faster than yours,
It has a louder horn,
It bumps other cars,
Our car's faster than yours.

My Mom's older than your Mom,
My Mom's older than yours,
She takes smelly baths
She hides the gray hairs
My Mom's older than yours.

Our car's older than your car,
Our car's older than yours,
It stops running and
Daddy kicks the fenders,
Our car's older than yours.

My Mom's funnier than your Mom,
My Mom's funnier than yours,
Her hair is pretty and
It changes colors,
My Mom's funnier than yours.
  (To Chorus)

AF

The Marvelous Toy

Words and Music by Tom Paxton © 1961 by Teena Music Corp.

When I was just a wee lit-tle lad full of health and joy, My fa-ther home-ward came one night and gave to me a toy. A won-der to be-hold it was, with man-y col-ors bright, And the mo-ment I laid eyes on it, it be-came my heart's de-light. It went 'zip' when it moved, and 'bop' when it stopped, And whirr when it stood still I nev-er knew just what it was And I guess I nev-er will.

Chorus

The first time that I picked it up I had
  a big surprise
For right on its bottom were two big
  buttons that looked like big green
  eyes.
I first pushed one and then the other,
  and then I twisted its lid
And when I set it down again, this is
  what it did:

It first marched left and then marched
  right and then marched under a
  chair
And when I looked where it had gone,
  it wasn't even there!
I started to sob and my daddy laughed,
  for he knew that I would find,
When I turned around, my marvelous
  toy, chugging from behind.

Well, the years have gone by too
  quickly, it seems, I have my
  own little boy
And yesterday I gave to him my
  marvelous little toy.
His eyes nearly popped right out of
  his head and he gave a squeal of
  glee,
Neither one of us knows just what it is,
  but he loves it, just like me.

Last Chorus:
It still goes Zip when it moves and
  Bop when it stops
And whir-r-r when it stands still,
I never knew just what it was
And I guess I never will.

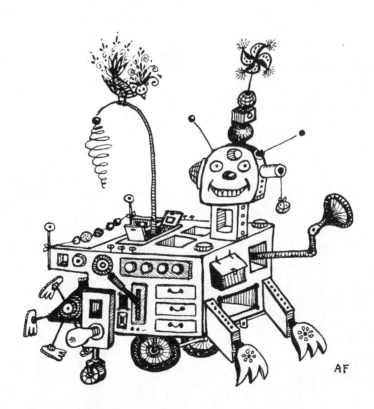

41

III.

STORY SONGS

Willie Seton - I know of no actual Willie Seton but the events, with variations, continue to this day. Now it's liquor stores they try for. Smarter men than I spend their lives trying to understand why. The Chad Mitchell Trio recorded this one.

John, John, John - John the Baptist was not the first man to lose his head over a woman and not the last one, either. Anita Carter does a good, rousing version of this one on a Mercury recording.

I'm the Man That Built the Bridges - Not a personal statement, I assure you; this song attempts to roll all the men who did build the nation into one Bunyan-like character. The Phoenix Singers and Peter Morse have done this one. Also me, on my Gaslight album.

Willie Seton

Words and Music by Tom Paxton © 1962 by Teena Music Corp.

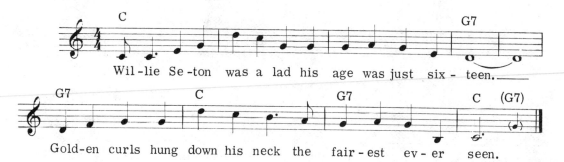

Wil-lie Se-ton was a lad his age was just six-teen.

Gold-en curls hung down his neck the fair-est ev-er seen.

His true love was the prettiest thing
    in the country-side,
And after Willie courted her,
She swore to be his bride.

He had no gold to give her dad,
No gold to buy them land.
And in his haste to wed his love,
He joined an outlaw band.

They ravaged all the country-side,
Their fortunes for to gain,
Until one cold and frosty day,
They robbed a Frisco train.

The train guard lost his life that day,
But just before he died,
He fired a deadly pistol ball,
In Willie Seton's side.

His comrades they deserted him,
And left him all alone.
And holding tightly to his side,
He started out for home.

He had not traveled many a mile,
Until the storm came on,
And Willie Seton found a log,
To set himself upon.

He leaned his back against a tree,
And held on to his side,
And in that cold and snowy wood,
Young Willie Seton died.

He was sixteen when he loved,
Sixteen when he cried,
Sixteen when he robbed the train,
And sixteen when he died.

AF

John, John, John

Words and Music by Tom Paxton © 1962 by Cherry Lane Music Inc.

John, the Bap-tist was a might-y man, He sanc-ti-fied my Lord, Preached the Gos-pel up and down the land, He sanc-ti-fied my Lord.

Lived in the des-ert and preached at the riv-er, John, John, John told the peo-ple 'bout the com-in' of Je-sus, John, John, John.__

(Chorus) It was John, John, John,__ It was John, John, John,__ It was John, John, John,__ that sanc-ti-fied my Lord.__ It was John, John, John,__ It was John, John, John,__ It was John, John, John__ that sanc-ti-fied my Lord.

Jesus came to the meetin' at the
river,
He sanctified my Lord,
John told Jesus to wade in the water,
He sanctified my Lord.
A dove flew down and landed on
Jesus,
John, John, John,
A voice said, "This is my son,
Emmanuel",
John, John, John. (It was...)

John told the people that the Saviour
was among them,
He sanctified my Lord,
Herod got angry and threw him in the
dungeon,
He sanctified my Lord,
Salome danced for the head of the
Baptist,
John, John, John,
Brought it in on a silver platter,
John, John, John. (It was....)

AF

I'm the Man That Built the Bridges

Words and Music by Tom Paxton © 1962 by Cherry Lane Music Inc

Chorus

I'm the man that built the brid-ges, I'm the man that laid the track, I'm the man that built this coun-try with my shoul-ders and my back. I'm the man that built the pow-er dams and oil-ed all the cars And I laid down the cor-ner-stone for this great land of ours. I cleared the rocks and tim-ber from the wild New Eng-land shore, And I la-bored long and hard to make it grow,____ And I built the first log ca-bins, and I raised a fam-i-ly, Told King George and all his Red-coats where to go.____

48

I'm the boy that drove the wagons
     when the people headed west,
Dug canals and pulled the barges on
     their way.
And I build and ran the fact'ries, cut
     the timber for your homes,
Drove the oxen when I cut and baled
     the hay.

I built the old sod shanties and I raised
     the prairie towns,
And I made the railroad run from sea
     to sea.
I raised and drove the cattle to feed a
     growing land,
And the mining towns are there
     because of me.

I stoked the mighty furnaces and
     rolled the flaming steel,
I operated oil rigs and wells.
And when the country needed them I
     built the planes and tanks,
To send the tyrants down to fry in
     hell.

My face it isn't pretty and my clothes
     are not the best,
And there ain't no big shots in my
     family tree.
But if you're wonderin' who it was
     that made this country great,
You don't have to look no further -- it
     was me.

IV.

YOU'VE GOT TO FEEL BAD SOMETIMES

Deep Fork River Blues - The Deep Fork is a muddy creek south of Bristow, Okla., where, when I was growing up, there was some fine hunting for swamp rabbits. I wrote this song on N.Y.'s Lower East Side, a long ways from the Deep Fork.

I Can't Help But Wonder (Where I'm Bound) - In any time, in any age, who can help but wonder?

Come Along Home - The first song of mine to be recorded - by The Chad Mitchell Trio.

Ramblin' Boy - One night last year I wrote three songs between shows at The Gaslight, threw two of them away and hung on to this one. It's been recorded by Pete Seeger, The Tarriers, Judy Collins, and I suppose it's my favorite.

Rain and Snow - I wrote this one with Woody and Cisco and their duets in mind. I tried singing it with Jack Elliott and it spoiled me for singing it any other way.

I'm On My Last Old Train - One of several dust-bowl songs I've been working on. Bristow, Oklahoma, my home, has many a ruined pasture where the top soil washed away or was blown away. It's one sad sight.

I'm Bound For the Mountains and the Sea - A big and beautiful country that some folks can never see enough of.

Fare Thee Well, Cisco - I only met him once, but I liked him. His brand of singing will be missed.

Deep Fork River Blues

Words and Music by Tom Paxton © 1962 by Cherry Lane Music Inc.

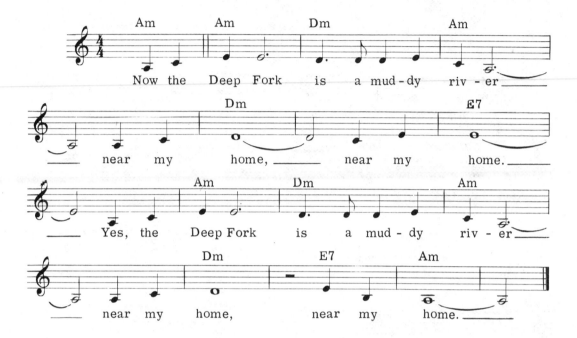

Now the Deep Fork is in Oklahoma
Near my home, near my home.
Yes, the Deep Fork is in Oklahoma
Near my home, near my home.

I can hear hounds baying on the river
Near my home, near my home
And I'll surely have a rabbit for my
    dinner
Near my home, near my home.

When the sun goes down a man gets
    awful lonesome
For his home, for his home.
When the sun goes down a man gets
    awful lonesome
For his home, for his home.

Well, I don't have to stay away forever
I can go home, I can go home
No, I don't have to stay away forever
I can go home, I can go home.

I Can't Help But Wonder
(Where I'm Bound)

Words and Music by Tom Paxton © 1963 by Cherry Lane Music Inc.

I have wandered through this land
Just a-doin' the best I can
Tryin' to find what I was meant to do.
And the people that I see
Look as worried as can be
And it looks like they are wonderin'
    too. (Chorus)

I had a little girl one time
She had lips like sherry wine
And she loved me till my head went
    plumb insane
But I was too blind to see
She was driftin away from me
And my good gal went off on the
    morning train. (Chorus)

And I had a buddy back home
But he started out to roam
And I hear he's out by Frisco Bay
And sometimes when I've had a few
His old voice comes singin' through
And I'm goin' out to see him some
    old day. (Chorus)

If you see me passing by
And you sit and you wonder why
And you wish that you were a rambler,
    too,
Nail your shoes to the kitchen floor
Lace 'em up and bar the door
Thank your stars for the roof that's
    over you. (Chorus)

AF

Come Along Home

Words and Music by Tom Paxton, © 1963 by Teena Music Inc.

1. Last night I heard a sweet voice call - in'.
2. Wind goes "Whoosh!" And the trees are sigh - in'.
3. Ev - 'ry night the voice gets bold - er.

Come a - long, won't you come a - long home. Wind on the riv - er and the
Come a - long, won't you come a - long home. Some - bod - y's born and some -
Come a - long, won't you come a - long home. Song gets sweet - er as

calves all bawl - in'. Come a - long, won't you come a - long home.
bod - y's dy - in'. Come a - long, won't you come a - long home.
I grow old - er. Come a - long, won't you come a - long home.

Chorus

Come a - long, won't you come a - long home now. Night is fall - in' and the

path is steep. ____ Come a - long, won't you come a - long home now.

Wa - ter's run - nin' and the riv - er is deep. ___ riv - er is deep. ___

AF

Ramblin' Boy

Words and Music by Tom Paxton © 1963 by Cherry Lane Music Inc.

He was a man _____ and a friend al -
ways _____ He stuck with me _____ in the hard old days. _____ He nev-er
cared _____ if I had no dough _____ We ram-bl'd 'round _____ in the rain and
snow. _____ And here's to you _____ my ram-blin' boy _____ May all your
ram - blin' bring you joy _____ And here's to you _____ my ram-blin'
boy _____ May all your ram - blin' bring you joy. _____

In Tulsa town we chanced to stray
We thought we'd try to work one day
The boss said he had room for one
Says my old pal, "We'd rather bum!"
   (Chorus)

Late one night in a jungle* camp
The weather it was cold and damp
He got the chills and he got 'em bad
They took the only friend I had.
   (Chorus)

He left me here to ramble on
My ramblin' pal is dead and gone
If when we die we go somewhere
I'll bet you a dollar he's ramblin'
    there. (Chorus)

* hobo jungle

New York

Rain and Snow

Words and Music by Tom Paxton © 1963 by Cherry Lane Music Inc.

Chorus
Rain and snow, Cold winds blow, What can a poor boy do All a-lone and I can't go home, And I wish I was back with you, with you, And I wish I was back with you.

Verse
1. Slept last night in an old hay barn As cold as cold could be, And as I lay there fall-in' a-sleep I dreamed you were there with me.

I work in the fields and I work in the
    yards,
I work for a migrant's pay.
When the job is done I move right
    along
For they're hard on the ones that stay.

I spend my time in the low saloons
Nursing a glass of beer.
Broke and hungry and wondering why
And wishing that you were here.

I'll be your man, my sweet Sally Ann
I'll sure try to look after you.
But when they say that's all that they'll
    pay,
Well, what can a hungry man do?

Now the times are hard and the times
    are bad
And jobs are hard to find.
It's down this road on tired feet
With trouble on my mind.

I'm on My Last Old Train

Words and Music by Tom Paxton © 1962 by Cherry Lane Music Inc.

I'm on my last old train and gone ____ I'm
on my last old train and gone ____ So
buy me a bot-tle of beer, Morn-in' sun won't find me
here, I'm on my last old train and gone. ____

Better times, better times may come
    some day,
Better times, better times may come
    some day
Better times will be comin', they sure
    couldn't get no worse,
Better times, better times may come
    some day.

Bye bye, old buddies and pals, bye
    bye,
Bye bye, old buddies and pals, bye
    bye,
I hate to leave you this way, I'm just
    too broke to stay,
Bye bye, old buddies and pals, bye
    bye.

I hear that freight train whistle blow,
I hear that freight train whistle blow,
I hear that whistle blow, I got to pack
    my bag and go,
Bye bye, old buddies and pals, bye
    bye.

I'm Bound for the Mountains and the Sea

Words and Music by Tom Paxton © 1962 by Cherry Lane Music Inc.

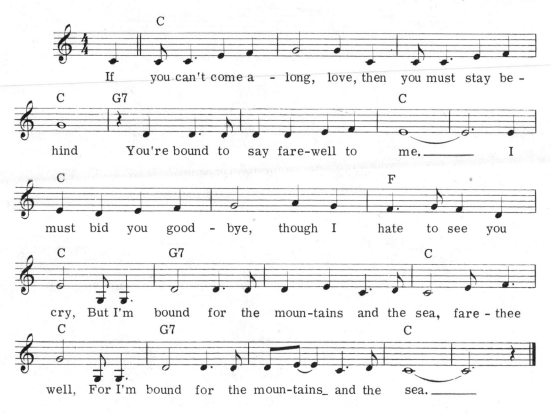

If you can't come a - long, love, then you must stay be -

hind You're bound to say fare-well to me._____ I

must bid you good - bye, though I hate to see you

cry, But I'm bound for the moun-tains and the sea, fare - thee

well, For I'm bound for the moun-tains_ and the sea._____

It's so hard to explain why I'm leaving
    once again,
It's nothing that I haven't done before.
It ain't nothin' much, I guess, but the
    thing I love the best
Is ramblin' this land from shore to
    shore, in this land,
Ramblin' this land from shore to
    shore.

I have walked, I have bummed, I've
    rode buses, I've rode trains,
I've ridden a time or two in a silver
    plane.
When I think of where I've been I just
    have to go again,
Just to see if everything is still the
    same, in this land
Just to see if everything is still the
    same.

So it's farewell, my dear, and I must
    be on my way,
There's many a thing that I must do
    and see.
I'm a mighty restless man in a mighty
    restless land
And I'm bound for the mountains and
    the sea, fare thee well,
I'm bound for the mountains and the
    sea.

Fare Thee Well, Cisco

Words and Music by Tom Paxton © 1963 by Deep Fork Music Inc.

While walk-ing through the rail-road yards on a cold and rain-y

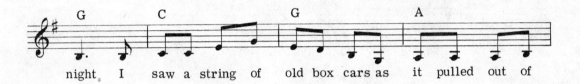

night, I saw a string of old box cars as it pulled out of

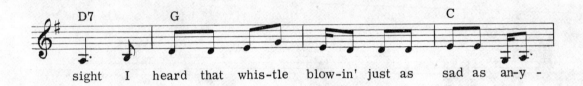

sight I heard that whis-tle blow-in' just as sad as an-y -

thing And it made me think of Cis-co and the songs he used to

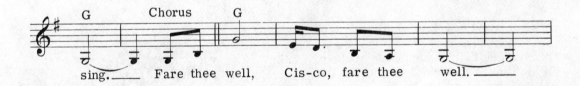

sing.___ Fare thee well, Cis-co, fare thee well.___

Here for just a - while, gone a man-y a mile.

Fare thee well, Cis-co, fare thee well.___

He walked down every highway in this
  great and mighty land,
He sang the songs of what he saw, he
  sang for every man,
He had no truck with nonsense, he
  sang 'em straight and plain,
He got his greatest music from the
  whistle of a train.
  (Chorus)

He rambled round with Woody, just
  to see what he could see,
And when the Fascist tide was high,
  he rambled out to sea,
And everywhere he rambled he made
  friends of many men,
And Cisco's friends can tell us we
  won't see his kind again.
  (Chorus)

I dreamed that me and Cisco, we
  were standing in some town.
The good clean air was in our lungs,
  the sun was shining down.
He said "This land has lots of room
  it stretches far and wide.
There's a lonesome freight at six-
  oh-eight
Let's grab that train and ride."
  (Chorus)

AF

63

V.

FURTHER PILLS TO PURGE MELANCHOLY

Bottle Of Wine - This one got started in Oklahoma and finished in Los Angeles, making it liable under the interstate laws. Judy Collins has recorded it on her concert album for Elektra.

I Happen To Like Whiskey, Sir! - Not a word of truth in the song, of course. Pure poetic license, you understand.

The Natural Girl For Me - The Lord knows I'm no woman hater, but sometimes, like the rest of us, they strike some pretty silly poses. Present company excepted, of course.

I'm Going To The Limelight To Die - I hope not, but it's possible. The Limelight is a watering hole on Seventh Avenue, much beloved by folksingers. It is also popular with its owners, Kelsey Marechal and Marty Lorin. Naturally, I wrote this song at Joe's Cafe on W. 4th St. I couldn't hear myself think over at the Limelight.

The N.Y. Mets Victory and Commiseration Song - The poor devils try so hard - who could help but love them? Dare I risk saying that there's a bit o' the Mets in all of us?

Willie My Weaver-o - A few years of hearing Ed McCurdy sing "dalliance" songs finally caught up with me in Champaign, Ill., and here's the result.

The Meanest Man In the World - Based on a very, very old joke. I thought it might make a good song. Jimmy Driftwood did the same thing when he wrote "The Unfortunate Man" - a very funny song.

Bottle of Wine

Words and Music by Tom Paxton © 1963 by Deep Fork Music Inc.

Chorus:
Bottle of wine, fruit of the vine,
When you gonna let me get sober?
Leave me alone, let me go home,
Let me go back and start over.

Ramblin' 'round this dirty old town,
Singin' for nickels and dimes,
Time's gettin' rough, I ain't got enough
To get a little bottle of wine.

Little hotel, older than hell,
Dark as the coal in a mine.
Blankets are thin, I lay there and
        grin,
'Cause I got a little bottle of wine.

Pain in my head, bugs in my bed,
Pants are so old that they shine.
Out on the street, tell the people I
        meet,
Won't you buy me a bottle of wine?

A preacher will preach, a teacher will
        teach,
A miner will dig in the mine,
I ride the rods, trusting in God,
Huggin' my bottle of wine.

I Happen to Like Whiskey, Sir!

Words and Music by Tom Paxton © 1962 by Cherry Lane Music Inc.

Verse C

1. As I was stand - ing at the bar, my
smiled and took ex - cep - tion, boys, to
He was so ex - cit - ed, boys, I

G7

el - bow bent in style. A white-haired gent stepped
my phil - os - o - phy. He said that all that
thought that he would burst. In his at - tempt to

C

up to me and faced me with a smile, He
whis - key, boys, would be the death of me, He
save me boys he'd worked up quite a thirst, He

C7 F

gent - ly chid - ed me and said that I would die in sin. I
told me of the ru - in it had brought to oth - er men. I
said he was so dog-gone dry he'd drink most an - y - thing. He

Chorus

G7 C

ord - er'd up a - noth - er round and this I said to him: "I
ord - er'd up a - noth - er round and said to him a - gain" I
drained the glass I gave him boys and he be - gan to sing:

C G7

hap - pen to like whis - key, sir, Now what's the harm in that? A

C

man must have a hob - by, sir, to keep from go - ing flat, I

C7

do not care for ten - nis, sir, I'm much too old and fat, I

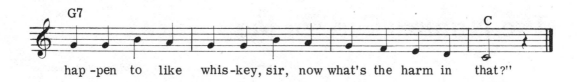

hap -pen to like whis-key, sir, now what's the harm in that?"

The Natural Girl for Me

Words and Music by Tom Paxton © 1963 by Deep Fork Music Inc.

Verse

C
All o-ver this great big ci-ty

F
can't find a wo-man who's nice and pret-ty,

G7   C
They all look like a page in a mag-a-zine._____

C
Legs are long and they eat like a spar-row,

F
Fig-ures stick to the straight and nar-row,

Top and bot-tom are the same as in be-tween.

Chorus

F
Show me a pret-ty lit-tle num-ber,

C
When she walks, she rolls like thun-der,

G7   C
Eyes as deep and dark as the deep blue sea,

70

Round   right   here   and   round   right   there

Pret - ty   red   lips   and   her   ver - y   own   hair,

Wrap her   up, she's the nat - u - ral   girl   for   me.

Way down in a coffeehouse palace
Found a little lady and her name was
    Alice
She had friends and her friends had
    her, it seems.
Face was dirty and her sweater was
    baggy
Pants were tight and her hair was
    shaggy, (I've)
Seen her kind on college football
    teams.

Chorus:
Show me a pretty little number, etc.

Way up in a penthouse pretty
Thirteen miles up above the city
I met a lady from a wealthy family.
She could cuss like a real longshore-
    man,
She was making eyes at the doorman
She made a most unusual offer to me.

Chorus:
Show me a pretty little number, etc.

Way up at a Broadway party
I met a lady who was very arty
She took me home to see her studio
She took out her paints and whispered
    to me
She said she wanted to "Do Me"
And some of that paint will never come
    off, I know.

Chorus:
Show me a pretty little number, etc.

AF

I'm Going to the Limelight to Die

Words and Music by Tom Paxton ©1964 by Deep Fork Music Inc

As I was out walk-ing through old Green-wich Vil-lage, I met an old man with a tear in his eye. He'd done with the world, in a last blaze of glo-ry, He was goin' to the Lime-light, to the Lime-light to die.

Chorus

Oh, Kel-sey and Mar-ty, the "A" train be damned! The "A" train be damned! The "A" train be damned! Kel-sey and Mar-ty the "A" train be damned! I'm going to the Lime-light to die! _____

"The Limelight," he said, "is the
     home of the Clancys,
The screech of the bagpipe resounds
     through the hall.
In the rumble and clatter of all of
     these lunatics
Nobody notices poor me at all."

"These bagpipes I spoke of: A
     clever invention,
A weapon more sinister than you
     might think.
Both Kelsey and Marty encourage the
     blowin' of 'em
Knowin' it will drive the poor devils
     to drink."

I followed the poor man to the depths
     of the Limelight.
The sight of Seventh Avenue he'd
     see never more.
For he took but one bite of the day's
     special dinner
And, smiling serenely, dropped dead
     on the floor.

The N.Y. Mets Victory and Commiseration Song

Words and Music by Tom Paxton © 1962 by Cherry Lane Music Inc.

They're devoted to their duties and
    they never shun nor shirk
They are ready day and night to give
    their all
With no sacrifice too great
On occasion here of late
A Met has been known to hit the ball.

Their direction is supreme and their
    management superb
And Casey's clear instructions loudly
    ring
The situation well in hand
He will call out his command
And no one understands a goddam
    thing.

Well, the Mets are here to stay and
    they've won the whole town's
    hearts
And the love we bear for them will
    never end
For the Yanks have lost their sheen
Since we found our own ball team
The New York Mets - the team that
    needs a friend.

Willie My Weaver-O

Words and Music by Tom Paxton © 1963 by Deep Fork Music Inc.

He's my dear weaver-O
He weaves my woes away
He is my shuttle and I am his loom
Down in some shady glen
Or in some quiet place
He does his weaving wherever there's
room. (Chorus)

I love my Willie and
He is my candy-O
His weaving fills me completely with
sighs
I long to go again
Out with my Willie - O
And watch him weave with the sun in
my eyes. (Chorus)

The Meanest Man in the World

Words and Music by Tom Paxton ©1962 by Cherry Lane Music Inc.

There was an old far-mer in our town, Beans in the ket-tle are boil-in'____ There was an old far-mer in our town Beans gon-na boil a-way____ ____ His beard was black, his face was red, Sand fleas flew a-round his head No-bod-y lis-tened to what he said, The mean-est man in the world. ____

This mean old farmer took him a wife,
Beans in the kettle are boilin'
This mean old farmer took him a wife,
Beans gonna boil away.
She was little and pretty and gay,
Never had very much to say,
He threw her in the wagon and drove
    away,
The meanest man in the world.

He scowled and mumbled as they
    rode on,
Beans in the kettle are boilin',
He scowled and mumbled as they
    rode on,
Beans gonna boil away.
They rode home in the evenin' sun,
The poor mule tripped and the son-of-
    a-gun
Cracked his whip and said, "That's
    one!",
The meanest man in the world.

They rode on another mile,
Beans in the kettle are boilin',
They rode on another mile,
Beans gonna boil away.
The mule fell again and threw a shoe,
The farmer's face was red and blue.
He muttered under his breath,
    "That's two!",
The meanest man in the world.

They rode a little further on down
    the road,
Beans in the kettle are boilin',
They rode a little further on down the
    road,
Beans gonna boil away.
Mule fell again and the farmer said,
    "Three!",
Shot him dead and his poor wife, she
Protested to the farmer. "That's
    one!", said he,
The meanest man in the world.

VI.

LOVE SONGS

My Lady's A Wild Flying Dove -

Ev'ry Time (When We Are Gone) -

Please Let Me Stay With You -

The Last Thing On My Mind -

My Lady's A Wild Flying Dove

Words and Music by Tom Paxton © 1963 by Cherry Lane Music Inc.

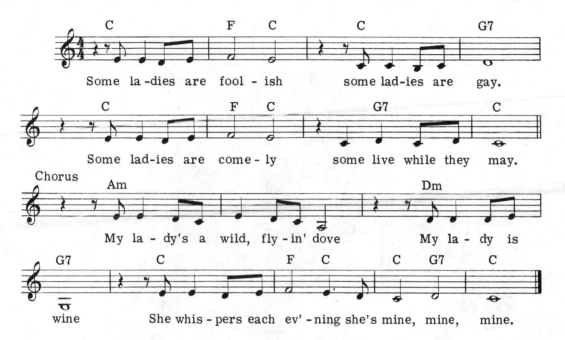

Some la-dies are fool-ish some lad-ies are gay.

Some lad-ies are come-ly some live while they may.

Chorus

My la-dy's a wild, fly-in' dove My la-dy is

wine She whis-pers each ev'-ning she's mine, mine, mine.

She likes pretty pictures
She loves singin' birds
She'll watch them for hours
But I see only her.

She tells me she's learning
How full her cup can be
She asks me to help her
But I know she's teaching me.

AF

Ev'ry Time (When We Are Gone)

Words and Music by Tom Paxton ©1962 by Cherry Lane Music Inc.

Very freely

1. Ev - 'ry time I hear a sweet bird
. Ev - 'ry time I hear your soft voice

sing - in' I think of you and I, my dear, I
hum - min' My heart jumps in my breast, my dear, my

think of you and I. When I hear the
heart jumps in my breast. And un - til I

eve - nin' bells a - ring - in' I hang my head and
hear your foot - steps com - in' I sure can know no

cry, my dear, I hang my head and cry.
rest, my dear, I sure can know no rest.

Chorus

And they will ring, And they will
I will love you, And I they will love

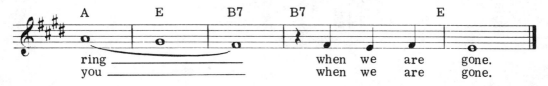

ring _____ when we are gone.
you _____ when we are gone.

Please Let Me Stay With You

Words and Music by Tom Paxton ©1963 by Deep Fork Music Inc.

Verse

If you'll be so kind, you can pac-i-fy my mind,
One kind fav-or let me ask of you oh hon-ey, I ain't got so long,
Can't tell right from wrong, hon-ey, Please, let me stay with you.

Make me up a bed where I can lay my
head,
I need you to tell my troubles to,
Oh, honey, just before I go,
Please let your hair hang low,
Honey, please let me stay with you.

I can feel a pain,
Running 'round my brain,
You don't know what I've been going
through,
Oh, honey, I'll be on my way,
Before the break of day,
So won't you please let me stay with
you.

In the morning light,
I'll move out of sight,
Who knows what I'll see or what I'll
do?
Oh, honey, I could love you so,
If you just don't make me go,
Honey, please let me stay with you.

I might shed a tear,
Miles away from here,
Some lonely evening when I'm feeling
blue,
Oh, honey, I might catch a train,
And come riding back again,
So, honey, please let me stay with
you.

The Last Thing on My Mind

Words and Music by Tom Paxton © 1964 by Deep Fork Music Inc.

It's a les-son too late for the learn-ing,___ Made of
sand, made of sand. In the wink of an eye my soul is
turn-ing,___ in your hand in your hand. Are you
go-ing a-way with no word of fare-well? Will there
be not a trace left be-hind? Well, I could have loved you bet-ter, did-n't
mean to be un-kind, You know that was the last thing on my mind.

As we walk, all my thoughts are
     a-tumblin',
'round and 'round, 'round and 'round.
Underneath our feet the subway's
     rumblin',
Underground, underground.

You've got reasons aplenty for goin',
This I know, this I know.
For the weeds have been steadily
     growing,
Please don't go, please don't go.

As I lie in my bed in the morning,
Without you, without you.
Each song in my breast dies
     a-borning,
Without you, without you.

DISCOGRAPHY

A JOB OF WORK TO DO
Tom Paxton, Ramblin' Boy (Elektra EKL-277)

A RUMBLING IN THE LAND
Tom Paxton, Ramblin' Boy (Elektra EKL-277)

THE WILLING CONSCRIPT
Pete Seeger, Broadsides (Broadside BR 302)
Tom Paxton, Newport Broadside (Vanguard VRS-9144)

THE HIGH SHERIFF OF HAZARD
Tom Paxton, Ramblin' Boy (Elektra EKL-277)

STRANGE RAIN
Robbins and Paxton (Rori)
Bobby Darin (Capitol)

WHAT DID YOU LEARN IN SCHOOL TODAY?
Pete Seeger, We Shall Overcome (Columbia CL 2101/CS 8901)
Pete Seeger, Broadsides (Broadside BR 302)
Chad Mitchell Trio, Reflecting (Mercury SR 60891/MG 20891)
Tom Paxton, Ramblin' Boy (Elektra EKL-277)

STANDING ON THE EDGE OF TOWN
Tom Paxton, Ramblin' Boy (Elektra EKL-277)

DAILY NEWS!
Tom Paxton, Ramblin' Boy (Elektra EKL-277)

WHEN MORNING BREAKS
Tom Paxton, Ramblin' Boy (Elektra EKL-277)

THERE WAS A TIME
Phoenix Singers (Warner Bros.)

GOIN' TO THE ZOO
Tom Paxton, Ramblin' Boy (Elektra EKL-277)

MY DOG'S BIGGER THAN YOUR DOG
Inman and Ira (Mercury)
Peter Morse, Goin' Down to Town (Philips PHS 600-059)

THE MARVELOUS TOY
Chad Mitchell Trio, Singin' Our Minds (Mercury SR 60838/MG 20838)

WILLIE SETON
Chad Mitchell Trio, Singin' Our Minds (Mercury SR 60838/MG 20838)

I'M THE MAN THAT BUILT THE BRIDGES
Phoenix Singers, The Phoenix Singers (Warner Bros. W 1485)
Peter Morse, Goin' Down to Town (Philips PHS   600-059)

MY RAMBLIN' BOY
Pete Seeger, The Weavers Reunion at Carnegie Hall (Vanguard VSD-2150)
Tom Paxton, Ramblin' Boy (Elektra EKL-277)
Judy Collins, The Judy Collins Concert (Elektra EKL-280)
The Kingston Trio (Decca)

I CAN'T HELP BUT WONDER WHERE I'M BOUND
Tom Paxton, Ramblin' Boy (Elektra EKL-277)
Carolyn Hester, That's My Song (Dot DLP 3604)
The Kingston Trio (Decca)

EVERYTIME
Carolyn Hester, That's My Song (Dot DLP 3604)
Patrick Sky, Patrick Sky (Vanguard VRS-9179)

COME ALONG HOME
Chad Mitchell Trio, The Chad Mitchell Trio at the Bitter End (Kapp KL-1281)

THE LAST THING ON MY MIND
Tom Paxton, Ramblin' Boy (Elektra EKL-277)
Mitchell Trio, Typical American Boys (Mercury SR 60992/MG 20992)

THE NATURAL GIRL FOR ME
Mitchell Trio, Typical American Boys (Mercury SR 60992/MG 20992)

BOTTLE OF WINE
Judy Collins, The Judy Collins Concert (Elektra EKL-280)
The Kingston Trio (Decca)

TOUGH LITTLE SOLDIER OF MINE
Carolyn Hester, That's My Song (Dot DLP 3604)

JOHN, JOHN, JOHN
Anita Carter, Anita Carter (Mercury SR 60847/MG 20847)

SONG INDEX

Page

67   Bottle of Wine

56   Come Along Home

53   Deep Fork River Blues

20   Dogs of Alabama, The

83   Ev'ry Time (When We Are Gone)

62   Fare Thee Well, Cisco

34   Going to the Zoo

10   Great American Dream, The

22   High Sheriff of Hazard, The

54   I Can't Help But Wonder (Where I'm Bound)

68   I Happen to Like Whiskey, Sir!

14   I Read It in ''The Daily News;''

61   I'm Bound for the Mountains and the Sea

72   I'm Going to the Limelight to Die

60   I'm on My Last Old Train

48   I'm the Man That Built the Bridges

17   Job of Work to Do, A

46   John, John, John

85   Last Thing on My Mind, The

36   Let's Pretend

33   Little Brand New Baby

40   Marvelous Toy, The

76   Meanest Man in the World, The

38   My Dog's Bigger Than Your Dog

81   My Lady's A Wild Flying Dove

74   N. Y. Mets Victory and Commiseration Song

70   Natural Girl for Me, The

84   Please Let Me Stay With You

57   Ramblin' Boy

59   Rain and Snow

28   Rumbling in the Land, A

12   Six Men Riding

27   Standing on the Edge of Town

21   Strange Rain

16   There Was A Time

9   Thresher Disaster, The

24   What Did You Learn in School Today?

13   When Morning Breaks

75   Willie My Weaver-O

45   Willie Seton

18   Willing Conscript, The